AQA GCSE (9-1) Spanish Vocabulary Crosswords

74 crossword puzzles covering core vocabulary for exams in 2018 onwards

Samiul Hassan

Lychee Publishing

First published in 2020 by
Lychee Publishing
info@lycheepublishing.com
www.lycheepublishing.com

This book is not endorsed by AQA. Lychee Publishing acknowledges that the publication of this book was made possible by AQA for granting permission for use of its materials.

Cover design by Millie Bicknelle

ISBN: 978-1-8382721-1-1

A catalogue record for this book is available from the British Library.

Introduction

So you're taking GCSE Spanish, or perhaps you're just interested in brushing up on your Spanish. Whatever the reason, this book will help you learn over 1,400 words and phrases and put your Spanish vocabulary to the test by tackling crossword puzzles. The themes and vocabulary covered in this book are aimed principally at students undertaking AQA GCSE (9-1) Spanish, for exams in 2018 and beyond.

Learning long lists of vocabulary and trying to recall words in a foreign language isn't always such an easy task. One thing is for sure, we all learn in different ways. Some find rote learning of words quick and effective, while others struggle through the mind-numbing task. In modern times, language learners have an extensive range of techniques at their disposal to help them learn vocabulary. One effective yet no-so-modern method that aids learners improve their command of a foreign language (and even their native language) is by playing crossword puzzles. Language learning doesn't have to be boring, and solving crosswords is a fun way to expand your vocabulary without treating it as a chore. It is also commonly known that crossword puzzles can help improve your mental health and relieve stress, so what are you waiting for?

Things to note before you get started

The puzzles in this book are designed to act as a supplementary learning aid in line with the specific course specification. The vocabulary covered in this book is not exhaustive. Students are advised to use this book in conjunction with other suitable learning materials and to consult the specification or their teacher for more information on course-related enquiries.

Articles (*un*, *una*, *el*, *la*, *los*, *las*) are not included in the solutions to clues unless they are part of phrases.

Where solutions to clues contain any words that can be expressed in different gender forms, the masculine form is assumed.

Solutions may be repeated within a given puzzle, as some Spanish words can have multiple meanings depending on the context, just like in English. Some clues and solutions may also be repeated across several puzzles where they apply to more than one theme.

Contents

Comparisons and conjunctions

ACROSS

1 like (4)

3 for that reason, therefore (3,3)

7 less than (5,3)

8 if (2)

10 more than (3,3)

11 to compare (8)

13 as, since (2,3)

15 so much, so many (5)

16 too, too much (9)

17 sufficient, enough, quite (8)

DOWN

1 as, like (4)

2 same (5)

3 like, similar to (8,1)

4 however (3,7)

5 because (6)

6 while, meanwhile (8)

9 so, therefore (3,3)

10 main, major, larger, bigger, greater (5)

12 not very, not much (4)

14 also (7)

ACROSS

1 none, no-one (7)

5 but, except (4)

6 from, of (2)

7 given that (4,3)

8 for (4)

10 in (2)

14 until (5)

17 on the other hand (3,4,4)

18 moreover, besides (6)

20 in other words, that is to say (2,5)

DOWN

1 nobody (5)

2 neither (… nor) (2)

3 nothing (4)

4 on the one hand (3,2,4)

5 according to (5)

9 neither/not … either … (7)

11 never (5)

12 not any more (2,2)

13 apart from (6,2)

14 towards (5)

15 without a doubt (3,4)

16 of course (5,3)

17 through, by, in, for, per (3)

19 without (3)

Important verbs

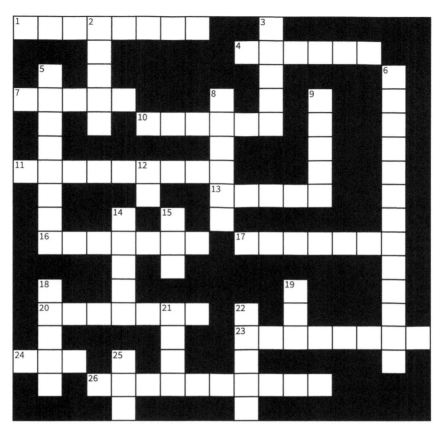

ACROSS

1 I'd like (8)

4 one must, one has to (3,3)

7 to be able, can (5)

10 to continue, to follow (6)

11 to need (9)

13 to throw (5)

16 to begin, to start (7)

17 to become, to turn into (7)

20 to happen (7)

23 to have just (done something) (6,2)

24 to be (description) (3)

26 to need, to be necessary (5,5)

DOWN

2 to know (a fact) (5)

3 to do, to make (5)

5 to become (8)

6 to realise (5,6,2)

8 to want, to love (6)

9 to put (5)

12 to go (2)

14 must, have to (5)

15 to give (3)

18 to regularly do something (5)

19 to go to (do something) (2,1)

21 to go away, to leave (4)

22 to happen, to spend (time) (5)

25 there is, there are (3)

4 Cardinal/ordinal numbers and expressions (1)

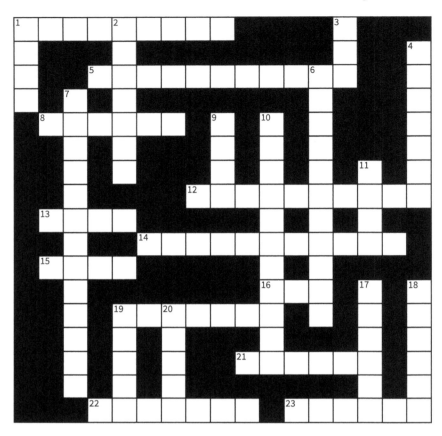

ACROSS

 1 one hundred and one (6,3)
 5 seven hundred (11)
 8 fifth (6)
12 twenty-eight (10)
13 twelve (4)
14 three hundred (11)
15 ten (4)
16 one (3)
19 fourteen (7)
21 twenty (6)
22 ninety (7)
23 eighth (6)

DOWN

 1 one hundred (4)
 2 thirty (7)
 3 two (3)
 4 first (7)
 6 eight hundred (11)
 7 four hundred (13)
 9 eleven (4)
10 twenty-nine (11)
11 eight (4)
17 dozen (6)
18 four (6)
19 five (5)
20 thirteen (5)

Cardinal/ordinal numbers and expressions (2)

ACROSS

1 seven (5)
3 pair, couple (3)
4 sixth (5)
6 fourth (6)
8 thirty-two (7,1,3)
13 one thousand (3)
15 nine (5)
16 eighteen (9)
18 second (7)
19 fifty (9)
20 about, approximately (4)
21 seventh (7)

DOWN

2 third (7)
5 three (4)
7 fifteen (6)
9 number (6)
10 eighty (7)
11 tenth (6)
12 sixteen (9)
14 twenty-one (9)
17 six (4)

ACROSS

1 why? (3,3)
7 how much? (6)
8 who? (5)
9 when? (6)
12 where from? (2,5)
16 how much does it cost (worth)? (6,4)
17 what colour? (2,3,5)
18 how many? (7)

DOWN

1 through where? (3,5)
2 what date? (3,5)
3 what? (3)
4 what time is it? (3,4,2)
5 for how long? (3,6,6)
6 how much is it? (6,2)
10 at what time? (1,3,4)
11 how? (4)
13 whose? (2,5)
14 what day? (3,3)
15 which? (4)

Greetings and exclamations

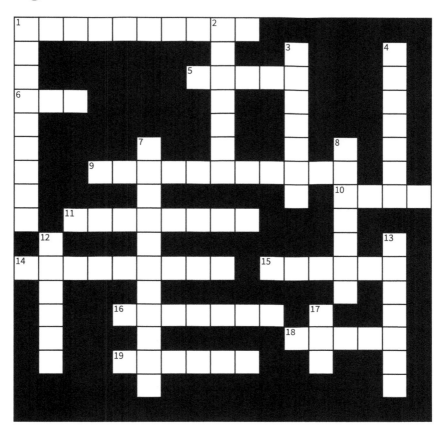

ACROSS

1 excuse me (3,7)

5 Of course! (5)

6 Watch out! Careful! (3)

9 Good luck! (5,6)

10 ok (4)

11 I'm sorry (2,6)

14 Have a good trip! (4,5)

15 you're welcome/don't mention it (2,4)

16 to greet, to say hello (7)

18 Come on! Rubbish! Nonsense! (3,2)

19 sorry (6)

DOWN

1 How are you? (4,5)

2 regards, greetings (7)

3 Help! (7)

4 till/see you (Monday) (5,2)

7 Best wishes! Congratulations! (11)

8 Really? (2,5)

12 What's up? (3,3)

13 That's enough! (5,2)

17 What a …! (3)

ACROSS

1 strange, rare (4)

4 awful, fatal (5)

6 to be interested in (11)

8 disappointed (12)

10 to make no difference (3,5)

13 new (5)

16 to take advantage of (12,2)

18 to adore, to love (6)

20 to agree, to reach an agreement (7,2,7)

21 boring, bored (8)

DOWN

2 correct, appropriate (9)

3 to hate (5)

4 great, fantastic (9)

5 ugly (3)

7 silly (5)

9 to make the most (10)

11 to recognise (9)

12 to wish (6)

14 expensive (4)

15 bad (4)

17 unique, only, single (5)

19 to doubt (5)

Opinions (2)

ACROSS

1 different (8)
3 pleasant (9)
4 quality (7)
7 precious, beautiful (8)
9 to be worth the trouble (5,2,4)
14 to appreciate (8)
15 cheap (6)
16 simple, plain, straightforward (8)

DOWN

1 disappointing (13)
2 advantage (7)
5 impressive, striking (13)
6 to have a bad time (7,3)
8 to disappoint (11)
10 lucky (10)
11 to hope (7)
12 to enjoy (9)
13 deep, profound (8)

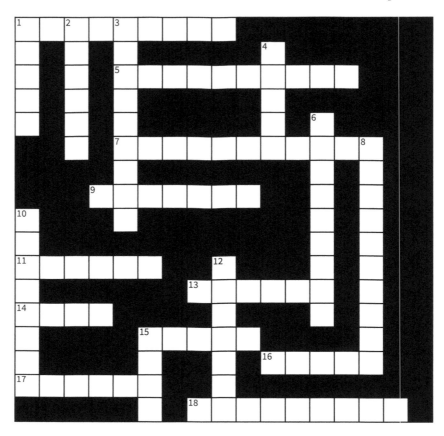

ACROSS

1 to annoy, to bother (9)

5 to be right (5,5)

7 exciting, thrilling, moving (11)

9 to seem (7)

11 safe, certain (6)

13 useless (6)

14 cool (4)

15 to say (5)

16 old (5)

17 to think, to give an opinion (6)

18 horrible (9)

DOWN

1 easy (5)

2 to feel (6)

3 to interest (9)

4 reason (5)

6 incredible (9)

8 fantastic, great, terrific (10)

10 unsafe, uncertain (8)

12 old (object) (7)

15 hard (4)

ACROSS

1 to be happy about (9,2)
6 surprised (11)
7 useful (4)
10 to delight (8)
11 to agree (5,2,7)

DOWN

1 to get bored (9)
2 to be in favour of (5,1,5)
3 amusing, entertaining (9)
4 to be against (5,2,6)
5 to believe (5)
8 fantastic, marvellous (9)
9 good (5)

ACROSS

1 next, following (9)
4 only (4)
5 again, once again (2,5)
6 month (3)
7 brief, short (5)
8 late (5)
9 while, short time (4)
11 per year (3,3)
13 before (5)
15 today (3)
16 every (4)
17 once (3)
18 seldom, a few times (5,5)
19 every month (5,3,5)

DOWN

1 always (7)
2 still, yet (7)
3 within (6,2)
4 on, around (5)
10 period, spell, season (9)
11 beginning (9)
12 twice (3,5)
14 afternoon, evening (5)
20 day (3)

ACROSS

1 autumn (5)
4 to take time (6)
5 morning (6)
7 during (7)
8 spring (9)
10 century (5)
12 past, previous (6)
14 slow (5)
16 at about … (1,3,2)
18 to last (5)
19 year (3)
20 future (8)
21 meanwhile (8,5)

DOWN

2 early (8)
3 it's been … (time) (4)
4 every week (5,3,7)
6 from time to time (2,3,2,6)
9 summer (6)
11 tonight (4,5)
13 since (5)
15 date (5)
17 night (5)

Expressions of time (3)

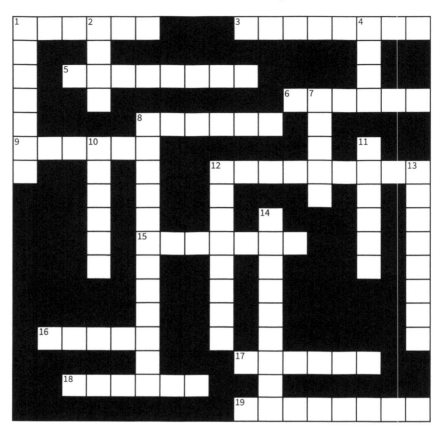

ACROSS

- **1** past (noun) (6)
- **3** then (8)
- **5** slowly (8)
- **6** last (6)
- **8** soon (6)
- **9** tomorrow (6)
- **12** straightaway (9)
- **15** again (4,3)
- **16** now, nowadays (5)
- **17** last night (6)
- **18** week (6)
- **19** Mondays (3,5)

DOWN

- **1** next (7)
- **2** yesterday (4)
- **4** nearly (4)
- **7** later, then, afterwards (5)
- **8** day after tomorrow (6,6)
- **10** sometimes, at times (1,5)
- **11** time (6)
- **12** season (8)
- **13** at/to the end of … (1,5,2)
- **14** at the moment, right now (2,7)

Location and distance

ACROSS

1 place (5)
6 east (4)
7 here (4)
9 straight (7)
10 over there (4)
11 against (6)
14 over there (far away) (4)
15 south (3)
16 straight ahead (4,5)
18 on the right, to the right (1,2,7)
20 on the left, to the left (1,2,9)
22 in front of (7,2)

DOWN

1 far away, distant, remote (6)
2 isolated (7)
3 west (5)
4 under, below (5)
5 outside of (5,2)
8 behind, at the back of (6,2)
11 nearby (7)
12 north (5)
13 around (9,2)
17 near (5)
19 behind, back (5)
21 there (3)

Colours, weights, measures and shape

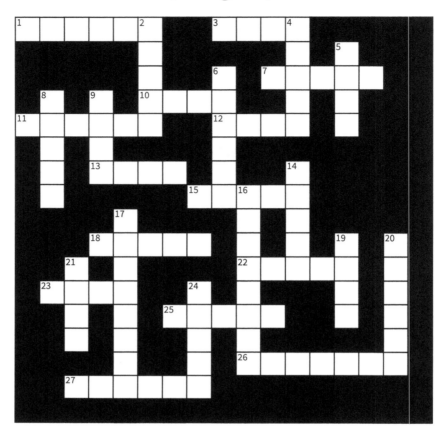

ACROSS

1 portion (6)
3 blue (4)
7 to measure (5)
10 pink (4)
11 size (6)
12 red (4)
13 tall, high (4)
15 wide (5)
18 light (pale) (5)
22 piece, slice (5)
23 box (4)
25 green (5)
26 slim, thin (7)
27 purple, violet (6)

DOWN

2 black (5)
4 full (5)
5 vivid, bright (4)
6 carton (6)
8 empty (5)
9 tin (4)
14 fat (5)
16 quantity (8)
17 to reach (8)
19 jar (4)
20 white (6)
21 low, short (4)
24 half (5)

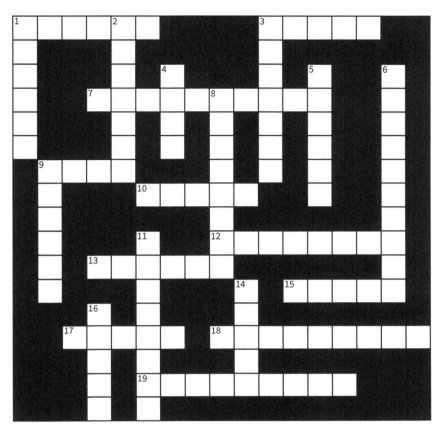

ACROSS

1 to rain (6)

3 to snow (5)

7 to be hot (5,5)

9 cloud (4)

10 to freeze (5)

12 hot, warm (8)

13 wind (6)

15 degree (5)

17 sky (5)

18 lightning (9)

19 clear (skies) (9)

DOWN

1 rain (6)

2 stable, steady, unchanged (7)

3 cloudy (7)

4 dry (4)

5 fresh (6)

6 stormy (10)

8 shower, downpour (8)

9 fog (6)

11 mild, temperate (8)

14 snow (5)

16 ice (5)

18 Access, correctness, materials and abbreviations

ACROSS

1 lie, untruth (7)
5 USA (4)
6 Miss (4)
8 fabric, material (4)
9 St (3)
12 Spanish railways (5)
14 engaged, occupied (7)
16 gold (3)
18 glass (6)
21 Mrs (3)
22 closed (7)
24 Dr (female) (3)
25 open (7)
26 wool (4)

DOWN

1 to tell a lie (6)
2 VAT (3)
3 high-speed train (3)
4 leather (5)
7 cotton (7)
9 silk (4)
10 avenue (4)
11 reason (5)
13 wrong (10)
15 pottery (8)
17 free, unoccupied (5)
19 Dr (male) (2)
20 wood (6)
23 badly (3)

Me, my family and friends (1)

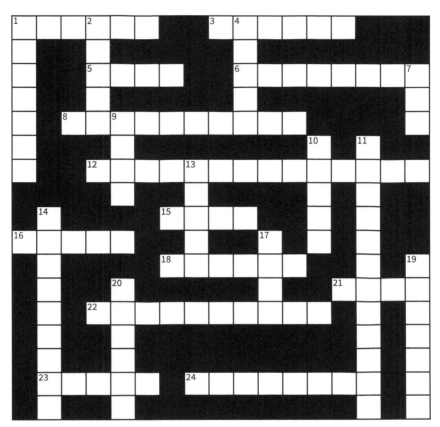

ACROSS

1 to receive, to welcome (6)
3 kind (6)
5 child (4)
6 retired (8)
8 to say goodbye (10)
12 to get on badly with (someone) (8,3,3)
15 mad (4)
16 fight (5)
18 polite (6)
21 hair (4)
22 rude (10)
23 widower (5)
24 memory (8)

DOWN

1 to agree on (7)
2 people (5)
4 wife, woman (5)
7 eye (3)
9 alone (4)
10 bald (5)
11 to miss someone (5,2,5)
13 nickname (5)
14 sporty (9)
17 face (4)
19 honest (7)
20 outing (6)

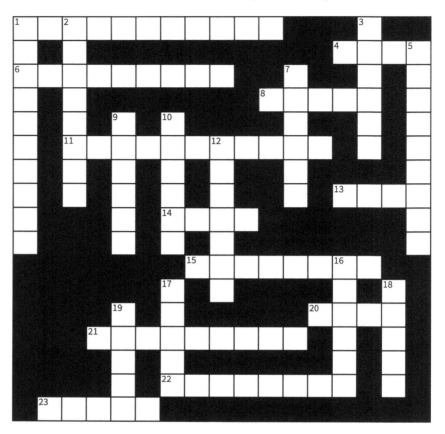

ACROSS

1 to have a birthday (7,4)
4 kiss (4)
6 to mistreat, abuse (9)
8 good-looking (5)
11 adolescent (11)
13 straight (hair) (4)
14 love (4)
15 to forgive (8)
20 wealthy (4)
21 stepmother (9)
22 last name (8)
23 children (5)

DOWN

1 engagement (10)
2 mistreatment, abuse (8)
3 jealous (6)
5 proud (9)
7 together (6)
9 polite, courteous (6)
10 to fight (6)
12 to know, to be familiar with (7)
16 ring (6)
17 beard (5)
18 short (5)
19 long (5)

ACROSS

1 sad (6)

5 greedy (6)

7 married (6)

11 party (6)

12 to be born (5)

15 stepfather (9)

18 to trust (7)

19 moustache (6)

22 weak (5)

24 selfish (7)

25 other people (5)

DOWN

2 broken (4)

3 serious, responsible (5)

4 to meet with someone (9)

6 uncle (3)

8 curly (6)

9 marital status (6,5)

10 relatives (9)

13 to get married (7)

14 cheeky, insolent, bold, daring (8)

16 man (6)

17 son (4)

20 glasses (5)

21 to be ... (years old) (5)

23 age (4)

ACROSS

1 young (5)
4 couple, partner (6)
7 mature (6)
9 to go out (5)
11 advice (7)
12 neighbour (6)
15 husband, spouse (6)
17 blonde (5)
19 dark (-haired, -skinned) (6)
20 wedding (10)
22 chestnut, brown (7)

DOWN

2 to look after, to deal with (8,2)
3 name (6)
4 red-haired (9)
5 careful (9)
6 young person (5)
8 gender (6)
10 nephew (7)
13 grandchild (5)
14 boyfriend (5)
16 old person (7)
17 to laugh (6)
18 baby (4)
21 free time, leisure (4)

ACROSS

1 kind, nice, pleasant (9)
5 naughty, mischievous (8)
6 grandfather (6)
9 understanding (adj) (11)
11 strong (6)
12 ear (5)
15 to bear, to put up with (8)
17 teenager (11)
19 affection (6)
20 happy (6)
21 home (5)
22 mean, miserly (5)

DOWN

2 to look like (9,1)
3 affectionate, tender (8)
4 husband (6)
7 freckles (5)
8 to look after (6)
10 brave, bold (8)
13 clumsy (5)
14 talkative (8)
16 lively (7)
18 idle, lazy (4)

ACROSS

1 happiness (9)

4 to kiss (5)

7 OAP, pensioner (8)

9 to break (6)

11 free time (6,5)

12 guest (8)

14 to bother (8)

15 youth, young people (8)

16 friendly (8)

17 trust (9)

DOWN

2 unpleasant (10)

3 to go for a walk (6)

5 birth (10)

6 marriage, married couple (10)

8 twin (6)

10 feeling (11)

13 outing, stroll, walk (5)

ACROSS

1 to thank (3,3,7)
9 cousin (5)
12 to feel like (5,5)
14 coward (7)
15 lad (8)
16 funny (8)

DOWN

1 argument (7)
2 to get on well with (someone) (8,4,3)
3 to smile (7)
4 get-together (7)
5 understanding (11)
6 dance hall, nightclub (4,2,7)
7 orphan (8)
8 to go for a stroll/ride (3,2,5)
10 lazy, idle (8)
11 appearance, looks (7)
13 to cry (6)

Technology in everyday life (1)

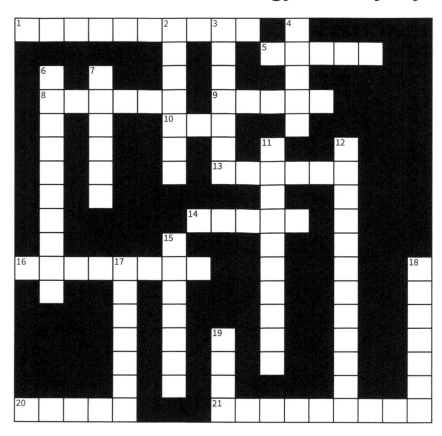

ACROSS

1 video game (10)
5 hyphen (5)
8 @ (6)
9 mouse (5)
10 network, internet (3)
13 risk (6)
14 to create (5)
16 bookmark (8)
20 dot, full stop (5)
21 computer (9)

DOWN

2 user (7)
3 to save (7)
4 mail box (5)
6 chat room (4,2,4)
7 to record, to burn (a disk) (6)
11 to block (screen) (10)
12 spam (6,6)
15 homepage (7)
17 file (7)
18 to surf (7)
19 wall (4)

Technology in everyday life (2)

ACROSS

1 to send (6)

7 to receive (7)

8 keyboard (7)

10 search engine (8)

11 load (6)

12 to attach (8)

14 browser (9)

15 to publish (8)

DOWN

2 digital magazine, e-magazine (7,7)

3 digital newspaper (9,7)

4 text message (7,2,5)

5 underscore (5,4)

6 social network (3,6)

9 to erase, delete (6)

13 to speak, talk (6)

ACROSS

1 track, court, run, slope, rink (5)
4 roast(ed) (5)
6 wine glass (4)
8 championship (10)
10 dish (5)
12 oil (6)
13 salt (3)
15 bicycle (9)
17 tuna (4)
20 to bring (5)
21 sail, sailing (4)
23 tip (7)
24 to fish (6)
25 to play (an instrument), to touch (5)

DOWN

1 film (8)
2 salami (10)
3 to swim (5)
4 garlic (3)
5 chicken (5)
7 performance, role (9)
9 stadium (7)
11 to drink (5)
14 cake, pie (6)
16 race (7)
18 ball (6)
19 meat (5)
20 tea (2)
22 lyrics (5)

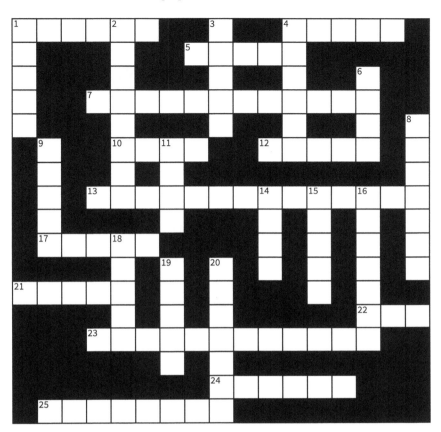

ACROSS

1 meal, lunch (6)
4 beef (5)
5 game, fun, amusement (5)
7 cured ham (5,7)
10 grapes (4)
12 strawberry (5)
13 to ride a horse (6,1,7)
17 milk (5)
21 sweet (5)
22 goal (3)
23 junk food (6,6)
24 sugar (6)
25 green pepper (8)

DOWN

1 pork (5)
2 breakfast (8)
3 cheese (5)
4 to run (6)
6 soup (4)
8 sport (7)
9 role (5)
11 suitable (4)
14 dinner (4)
15 dancing (5)
16 lettuce (7)
18 egg (5)
19 member (5)
20 cod (7)

Free-time activities (3)

ACROSS

1 snack/picnic (8)
3 vegetables, pulses (9)
4 pepper (8)
6 to lose (6)
9 nut, walnut (4)
11 cream (4)
13 beer (7)
14 sandwich (9)
16 cabbage (3)
18 outdoors (2,4,5)
19 tasty (4)
20 fish (7)
21 nibbles, bar snacks (5)
22 cup, trophy (4)

DOWN

2 grilled (1,2,7)
4 banana (7)
5 to ride a bike (6,2,4)
7 star (8)
8 soundtrack (5,6)
10 pineapple (4)
12 prawns (6)
15 boiled sweet (8)
17 billiards (6)

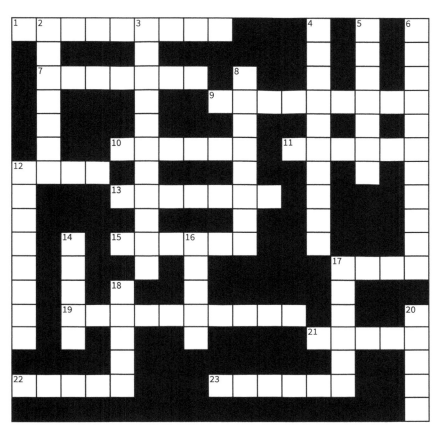

ACROSS

1 to queue (5,4)
7 toast (7)
9 police (adj) (9)
10 steak (6)
11 dessert (6)
12 glass (4)
13 lamb (7)
15 ice cream (6)
17 pear (4)
19 horse riding (10)
21 menu (5)
22 to order, ask for (5)
23 drink (6)

DOWN

2 artist (7)
3 mushrooms (11)
4 enthusiast (10)
5 spicy (7)
6 fruit juice (4,2,5)
8 contest, competition (8)
12 vegetables (8)
14 to eat (5)
16 to walk (5)
17 potato (6)
18 to play (5)
20 to win (5)

ACROSS

1 adventure sports (8,2,6)
5 to have the evening meal (5)
6 prize (6)
10 chop (7)
12 crème caramel (4)
15 seafood (8)
16 steak, fillet (6)
17 salty (6)
18 sauce (5)
19 omelette (8)

DOWN

1 sports person (10)
2 to taste, to try (6)
3 documentary (10)
4 cold soup (8)
7 news (8)
8 actress (6)
9 peas (9)
11 to cook (7)
12 show, performance (7)
13 lunch (8)
14 cuisine, cooking (6)

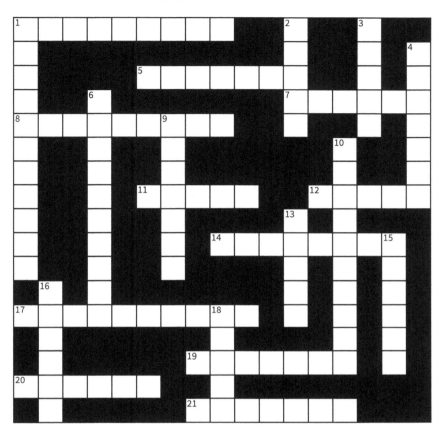

ACROSS

1 skateboard (9)
5 fritters (7)
7 to sing (6)
8 live (2,7)
11 rice (5)
12 fat (5)
14 skating (8)
17 basketball (10)
19 song (7)
20 to dance (6)
21 to skate (7)

DOWN

1 butter (11)
2 fishing (5)
3 fried (5)
4 hake (7)
6 white wine (4,6)
9 sausage (7)
10 loaf of bread (5,2,3)
13 ice (5)
15 to choose (6)
16 to score (a goal) (6)
18 plot (5)

ACROSS

1 toilets (9)

7 onion (7)

8 peach (9)

9 bill (6)

12 orange (7)

14 recording (9)

15 veal (7)

16 squid (9)

DOWN

2 show (11)

3 winner, champion (7)

4 player (7)

5 biscuit (7)

6 food, nourishment (12)

10 nothing else (4,3)

11 advert (7)

13 drums (7)

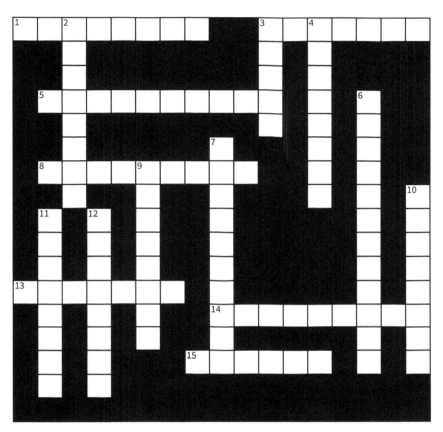

ACROSS

  1 to have lunch (8)
  3 fork (7)
  5 soap opera (10)
  8 carrot (9)
 13 spoon (7)
 14 team, side (9)
 15 tournament (6)

DOWN

  2 to have a snack/picnic (8)
  3 to have, to take (5)
  4 swimming (8)
  6 fast food (6,6)
  7 canoeing (10)
  9 story (8)
 10 singer (8)
 11 box office (8)
 12 knife (8)

ACROSS

  1 to be hungry (5,6)
  6 team, equipment (6)
  7 match (7)
 10 pastime, hobby, entertainment (9)
 12 ticket (7)
 13 to have breakfast (9)

DOWN

  1 to be thirsty (5,3)
  2 red wine (4,5)
  3 apple (7)
  4 cartoons (7,8)
  5 ice cream parlour (9)
  8 sporty (10)
  9 rosé wine (4,6)
 11 included (8)

Customs in Spanish-speaking countries

ACROSS

1 toy (7)

5 bullfight (7)

7 Father Christmas (4,4)

8 festival (6)

11 fancy dress (7)

16 fair (5)

17 statue paraded at Easter (4)

18 bullfighter (6)

DOWN

2 cowboy (6)

3 tomato throwing festival (8)

4 bull (4)

6 All Souls' Day (3,2,3,7)

9 to be lucky (5,6)

10 Christmas carol (10)

12 the Three Kings (5,5)

13 Mexican musician (8)

14 saint's day (5)

15 flag (7)

Home, town, neighbourhood and region (1)

ACROSS

- **1** to try on (8)
- **6** clean (6)
- **8** kitchen sink (9)
- **10** tobacconist's (7)
- **13** floor (5)
- **15** floor, storey (6)
- **17** to reduce (price, weight) (7)
- **18** to owe (5)
- **19** side (4)
- **20** inhabitant (9)

DOWN

- **1** to put on (clothes) (7)
- **2** handbag (5)
- **3** to go up (5)
- **4** microwave oven (10)
- **5** tie (7)
- **7** make-up (10)
- **9** shelves (10)
- **11** to sit down (8)
- **12** bathroom, WC (4)
- **14** lake (4)
- **15** door (6)
- **16** tree (5)
- **18** to look onto (3,1)
- **19** light (3)

ACROSS

- **1** lounge (5)
- **3** price (6)
- **6** blouse (5)
- **7** mirror (6)
- **10** bed (4)
- **11** square (5)
- **12** oven (5)
- **14** pocket money (4)
- **15** table (4)
- **16** cinema (4)
- **19** hairdresser's (10)
- **22** jeweller's (7)
- **24** sale (5)
- **25** ground floor (6,4)

DOWN

- **2** village (5)
- **4** cardigan (6)
- **5** shopping (7)
- **8** bridge (6)
- **9** bakery (9)
- **13** dishwasher (10)
- **16** comfortable, convenient, handy (6)
- **17** village, people, nation (6)
- **18** river (3)
- **20** sales (7)
- **21** window (7)
- **23** to pay (5)

Home, town, neighbourhood and region (3)

ACROSS

1 butcher's (10)
6 to wash (5)
7 fashion (4)
9 cap (5)
10 basement, cellar (6)
11 washbasin (6)
14 farm (6)
15 to tidy, to fix (8)
17 bull ring (5,2,5)
18 community (9)
19 clothes shop (6,2,4)

DOWN

1 change, exchange (6)
2 receipt (6)
3 police station (9)
4 bathroom, bath (4)
5 neighbourhood (6)
8 sports centre (13)
12 street (5)
13 own (6)
16 flower (4)

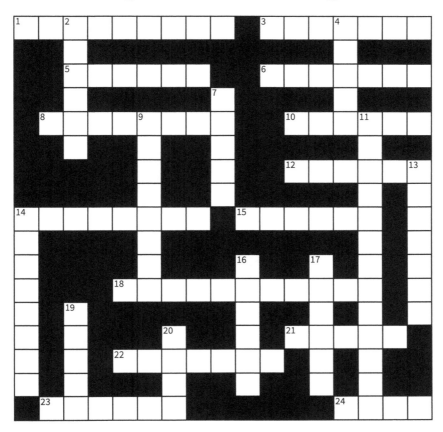

ACROSS

1 to queue (5,4)
3 furniture (7)
5 fridge (6)
6 to show (7)
8 wastepaper basket (8)
10 lawn (6)
12 plant (6)
14 purse (8)
15 shop (6)
18 heating (11)
21 watch (5)
22 tracksuit (7)
23 shirt (6)
24 thing (4)

DOWN

2 to count, to tell (6)
4 boots (5)
7 wall (5)
9 bookshop (8)
11 shorts (8,5)
13 wardrobe, cupboard (7)
14 mosque (8)
16 to spend money, to use (energy) (6)
17 money (6)
19 chair (5)
20 till (4)

Home, town, neighbourhood and region (5)

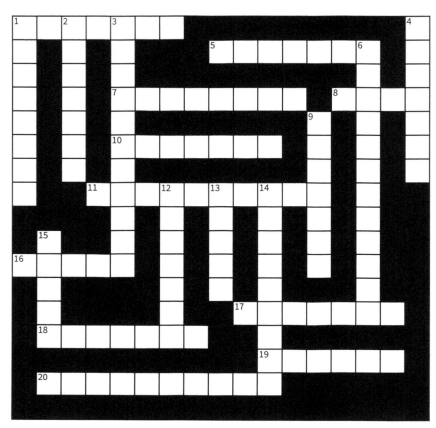

ACROSS

1 to suggest (7)
5 corner (7)
7 rent (8)
8 luxury (4)
10 shelf (7)
11 pastry shop (10)
16 size (clothes) (5)
17 dining room (7)
18 outskirts (7)
19 armchair (6)
20 bedroom (10)

DOWN

1 sweatshirt (8)
2 gloves (7)
3 designer clothes (4,2,5)
4 business (7)
6 town hall (12)
9 scarf (7)
12 terrace (7)
13 key (5)
14 refund (9)
15 blanket (5)

Home, town, neighbourhood and region (6)

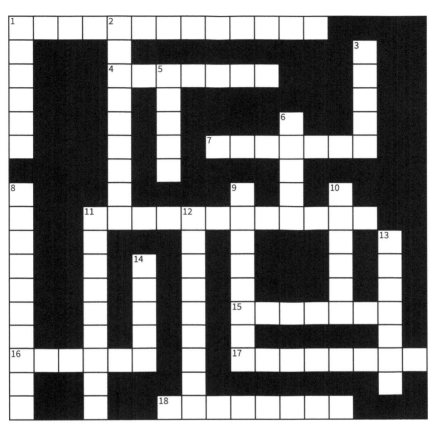

ACROSS

1 youth club (4,2,7)
4 market (7)
7 fitted carpet (7)
11 pedestrian zone/area (4,8)
15 entrance (7)
16 to go in, to enter (6)
17 to rent, to hire (8)
18 lift, elevator (8)

DOWN

1 to cut, to mow (6)
2 address, home (9)
3 shower (5)
5 noise (5)
6 museum (5)
8 library (10)
9 T-shirt (8)
10 court (e.g. tennis) (6)
11 shoe shop (9)
12 shutters, venetian blinds (9)
13 to give a present (7)
14 to go down (5)

ACROSS

1 church (7)
4 cent (7)
6 to move (house) (7)
7 bowling alley (6)
9 curtain (7)
12 floor, flat (4)
13 city (6)
15 size (6)
16 nightgown (7)
17 sales assistant (8)
18 coat (6)

DOWN

2 traffic lights (8)
3 forest, woods (6)
4 centre, down town (6)
5 theatre (6)
8 carpet (8)
9 socks (10)
10 to save (7)
11 tights (5)
13 jacket (bomber, leather) (8)
14 to be difficult/hard (6)

ACROSS

1 bathroom (6,2,4)
4 corridor (7)
5 range, supply, stock (7)
6 jeans (8)
10 washing machine (8)
11 dress (7)
14 necklace (6)
15 to do the shopping (5,2,6)

DOWN

2 parking (12)
3 noisy (7)
7 swimming costume (7)
8 umbrella (8)
9 landscape, scenery (7)
12 to return (8)
13 to wear (6)

ACROSS

- **1** to deliver (8)
- **5** advert, announcement (7)
- **6** port, harbour (6)
- **7** belt (8)
- **8** cash (8)
- **11** mountain range (6)
- **12** to sell (6)
- **14** rented (9)
- **15** stockings (6)

DOWN

- **2** earrings (10)
- **3** half price (1,5,2,6)
- **4** shoes (7)
- **9** factory (7)
- **10** skirt (5)
- **13** space (7)

Home, town, neighbourhood and region (10)

ACROSS

1 banknote (7)
6 bungalow, house (6)
11 building (8)
12 to buy (7)
13 countryside, grounds (5)
14 to share (9)

DOWN

2 pound sterling (5,9)
3 electrical appliances (17)
4 room (10)
5 entrance hall, lobby, foyer (9)
7 to build (9)
8 Post Office (7)
9 cooker, kitchen (6)
10 present, gift (6)

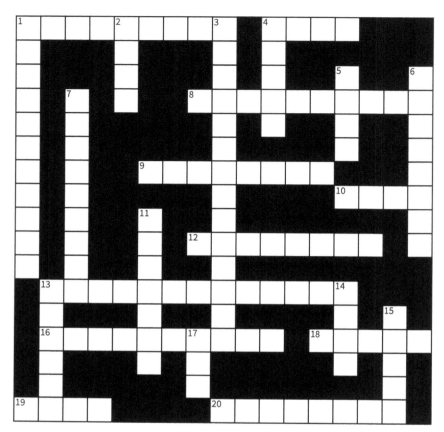

ACROSS

1 to do (for a living), to devote oneself (9)
4 AIDS (4)
8 voluntary (10)
9 drunk (8)
10 to smell (4)
12 to be ill (5,3)
13 training (13)
16 to be in pain (5,5)
18 pain, ache (5)
19 disgust (4)
20 to breathe (8)

DOWN

1 to wake up (11)
2 to fall down (4)
3 to feel ill (11,3)
4 health (5)
5 healthy, wholesome (4)
6 to fall asleep (8)
7 temptation (9)
11 brain (7)
13 stress (6)
14 smell (4)
15 to hurt (5)
17 NGO (3)

ACROSS

1 to get drunk (13)
5 smoke (4)
6 unhealthy (7)
7 to sleep (6)
8 life (4)
10 to feel sleepy (5,5)
13 cigarette (10)
14 joint (5)
15 not healthy (4,4)

DOWN

2 to die (5)
3 to get tired (8)
4 balanced (11)
9 to warn (8)
11 ill (7)
12 alive (4)

ACROSS

1 to contribute (10)
5 to cause, to provoke (8)
7 to smoke (5)
8 to avoid (6)
10 to injure, to harm (5,4)
12 volunteer (10)
13 to get better (9)
14 tired, tiring (7)
15 addiction to tobacco (10)

DOWN

2 respiratory (12)
3 stressing, stressful (10)
4 soft drug (5,6)
6 need (9)
9 overweight, obesity (9)
11 body (6)

Social issues (4)

ACROSS

1 hard drug (5,4)

3 smoker (7)

6 to be part of (6,5)

10 healthy (9)

DOWN

1 earache (5,2,5)

2 warning, notice (5)

3 passive smoker (7,6)

4 charity (4,8)

5 HIV positive (12)

7 dead (6)

8 disgusting (9)

9 drinking party in the street (8)

11 active (6)

ACROSS

1 dirty (5)
3 to turn off (lights etc) (6)
6 fire (5)
7 nature (10)
11 to fight, to combat (8)
14 harm, damage (4)
15 harmful (6)
18 jungle, tropical forest (5)
20 increase (7)
21 development (10)

DOWN

1 to save (6)
2 flood (10)
4 battery (4)
5 law (3)
6 lack (5)
8 scarce, meagre (6)
9 worrying (11)
10 cardboard (6)
12 global, world-wide (7)
13 theft, burglary (4)
16 to commit (7)
17 drought (6)
19 fault, blame, guilt (5)

Global issues (2)

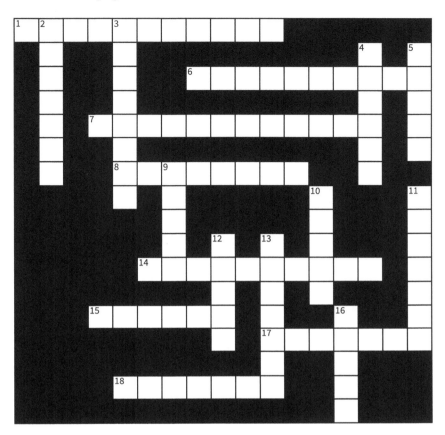

ACROSS

1 waste, rubbish, squandering (11)

6 to solve, to resolve (10)

7 to blame (5,2,5)

8 to ruin, to destroy (8)

14 worried, anxious (10)

15 to fight, to struggle (6)

17 unjust, unfair (7)

18 resource (7)

DOWN

2 shortage, want, lack (7)

3 to make dirty, to soil, to make a mess (8)

4 wrapping, packaging, container (6)

5 serious (5)

9 to steal (5)

10 to kill (5)

11 consumption (7)

12 poor (5)

13 chemical (adj) (7)

16 just, fair (5)

ACROSS

1 to ruin, to spoil (9)

4 campaign (7)

8 to benefit (10)

10 rubbish, garbage (6)

11 thief (6)

14 equality (8)

15 traffic jam (6)

18 witness (7)

19 to disappear (11)

DOWN

1 foreigner (10)

2 recycling (9)

3 to increase (8)

5 danger (7)

6 inequality (11)

7 to throw (away) (5)

9 to recycle (8)

12 Earth (6)

13 world (5)

16 to exhaust, use up (6)

17 fine (5)

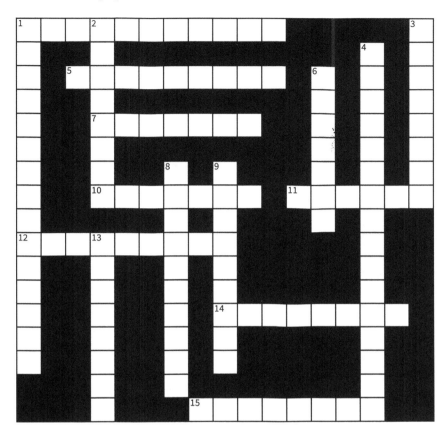

ACROSS

1 ozone layer (4,2,5)
5 renewable (9)
7 hole (7)
10 to collect, to gather, to pick up (7)
11 bird (6)
12 to waste, to misuse, to squander (9)
14 poll, survey (8)
15 hooligan, lout, troublemaker (8)

DOWN

1 climate change (6,9)
2 to threaten (8)
3 oil (8)
4 homeless people (8,3,5)
6 hurricane (7)
8 container (10)
9 oil tanker (9)
13 government (8)

ACROSS

1 to turn on (lights, TV etc) (8)
5 poverty (7)
6 to use (8)
10 fuel (11)
11 to be missing (6)
12 rechargeable (10)

DOWN

1 greenhouse effect (6,11)
2 crop (7)
3 rubbish, waste (8)
4 refuse, waste, rubbish (8)
5 prejudice (9)
7 to reuse (10)
8 violence (9)
9 dangerous (9)

ACROSS

1 Germany (8)

6 guide (4)

8 British (9)

10 track, lane (3)

13 souvenir (8)

16 sea (3)

17 camp site, camping (7)

20 to spend time, to go through, to pass (5)

22 sunstroke (10)

23 engine (5)

24 to stop (5)

DOWN

2 to ski (7)

3 island (4)

4 flight (5)

5 boat (5)

7 platform (5)

9 to cross (6)

10 to see (3)

11 South American (12)

12 France (7)

14 to wait (7)

15 unleaded (petrol) (3,5)

18 petrol (8)

19 airplane, aeroplane (5)

21 ID card (3)

ACROSS

1 North American (14)
8 single (room) (10)
9 to turn (6)
10 to bathe, to swim (7)
11 to take, to catch (5)
13 guidebook (4)
14 trip, journey (5)
16 sleeping bag (4,2,6)
18 to complain (8)

DOWN

2 on foot, walking (1,3)
3 to walk (7)
4 station (bus/coach/train) (8)
5 customs (6)
6 stop (6)
7 Greece (6)
9 rest, pause (8)
10 to look for (6)
11 helmet (5)
12 delay (7)
13 Wales (5)
15 to come (5)
17 underground (railway) (5)

ACROSS

1 beach (5)
3 railways (11)
5 driving licence (6,2,8)
9 lorry (6)
10 German (6)
11 sign, signal (5)
14 Welsh (5)
15 space, room (5)
16 car (5)
17 traveller (7)
18 fan (7)

DOWN

2 to arrive (6)
4 tent (6)
6 tram (7)
7 European (7)
8 to rest (9)
9 driver (9)
10 to lodge, to stay (8)
12 Spanish (7)
13 seat (7)

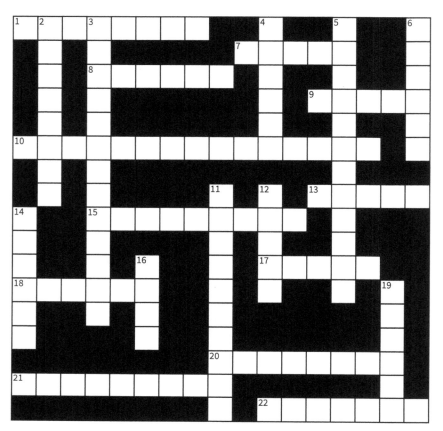

ACROSS

1 to book, to reserve (8)
7 registration form (5)
8 to turn, to twist (6)
9 to take photos (5)
10 underpass, subway (4,11)
13 skiing (5)
15 non-smoking (person) (2,7)
17 available, vacant (5)
18 Europe (6)
20 atmosphere (8)
21 trip, excursion (9)
22 coach (7)

DOWN

2 luggage (8)
3 United States (7,6)
4 to travel (6)
5 waiting room (4,2,6)
6 breakdown, fault (6)
11 Castillian (Spanish spoken in Spain) (10)
12 double (room) (5)
14 Greek (6)
16 country (4)
19 suitcase (6)

Travel and tourism (5)

ACROSS

1 place, site (5)
4 postcard (6)
7 travel agent's (7,2,6)
9 to go back (8)
10 leaflet, pamphlet (7)
13 mountain (7)
14 wheel (5)
15 arrival (7)
16 English (6)
17 card, postcard (7)

DOWN

2 Ireland (7)
3 London (7)
5 full board (7,8)
6 return (7)
8 boarding house (7)
11 ticket office (8)
12 Spain (6)

ACROSS

1 to get a tan (10)
5 camera (6)
7 path, route (6)
8 bus pass (7)
9 Irish (8)
11 reservation (7)
12 pass, card (6)
13 complaint (5)
14 Canary Islands (5,8)
15 facilities (13)

DOWN

2 to relax (9)
3 Scotland (7)
4 management (9)
6 youth hostel (8,7)
10 holidays (10)

ACROSS

1 on the right-hand side (1,4,7)
5 to lose, to miss (6)
6 to take (6)
7 Scot, Scottish (7)
10 crossroads, intersection (5)
12 passenger (8)
13 exit (6)
14 England (10)
15 to return (6)

DOWN

2 water sports (8,9)
3 cruise (7)
4 to park (7)
8 state owned hotel (in Spain) (7)
9 room (hotel) (10)
10 to change (7)
11 left luggage office (8)

ACROSS

1 French (7)
4 suncream (5,5)
6 to take time (6)
9 view (5)
11 to drive, to lead (8)
12 return (ticket) (3,1,6)
13 accommodation (11)
14 toilet paper (5,9)

DOWN

2 highway (9)
3 Great Britain (4,7)
5 to get lost (8)
7 available (10)
8 broken down (8)
10 sunshade, parasol (9)

My studies

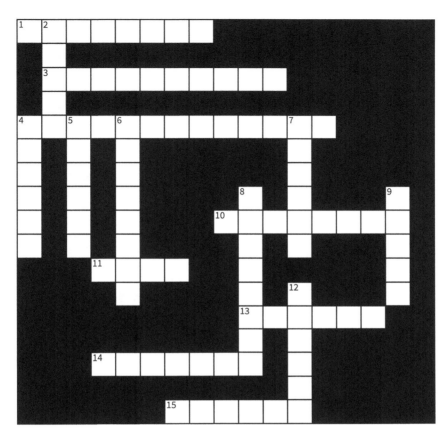

ACROSS

1 business studies (8)
3 hard working (10)
4 drama (4,9)
10 gymnastics (8)
11 mark (grade) (4)
13 language (6)
14 French (7)
15 attentive (6)

DOWN

2 to choose, to opt for (5)
4 German (6)
5 workshop (6)
6 head teacher, principal (8)
7 food technology (6)
8 science (8)
9 task, homework (5)
12 drawing/art (6)

ACROSS

- **1** disobedient (12)
- **7** to punish (8)
- **8** chewing gum (6)
- **9** test, proof (6)
- **11** bullying (5)
- **13** biology (8)
- **17** notes (7)
- **18** classroom (4)
- **19** to annoy, to bother (8)
- **20** school (7)

DOWN

- **1** office (8)
- **2** hall, assembly room (5,2,5)
- **3** educational (9)
- **4** intimidation, bullying (12)
- **5** to translate (8)
- **6** to listen, to hear (3)
- **10** reading (7)
- **12** to fail (exam/subject) (9)
- **14** to read (4)
- **15** gymnasium (8)
- **16** to help (6)

ACROSS

1 folder, file (7)

7 explanation (11)

10 rule, ruler (5)

12 to support, to back, to help (6)

16 to forget (7)

17 letter (of the alphabet) (5)

19 to design (7)

20 help, support, backing (5)

21 to approve, to pass (an exam) (7)

DOWN

1 to shut up, to be quiet (8)

2 answer (9)

3 to understand (8)

4 diary (6)

5 scissors (7)

6 secondary school, institute (9)

8 page (6)

9 to chat (7)

11 book (5)

13 permission (7)

14 level (5)

15 to be absent (6)

18 topic, theme (4)

ACROSS

1 sports field (5,2,8)
7 work (7)
8 lesson (7)
9 question (8)
12 to look (5)
13 summary (7)
14 absent (7)
15 help (5)

DOWN

2 to learn (8)
3 word (7)
4 pencil case (7)
5 assessment (10)
6 outstanding (13)
10 routine (6)
11 to draw (7)

ACROSS

1 pen (9)
3 rucksack, school bag (7)
4 behaviour, conduct (8)
6 to make an effort (10)
8 to finish (8)
11 to call the register (5,2,5)
12 to explain (8)
13 staffroom (4,2,10)
14 to hit (7)

DOWN

2 to fail (8)
5 to borrow (5,8)
7 to revise (7)
9 examination (6)
10 mistake, absence (5)

ACROSS

1 masculine (9)
5 to ask a question (9)
6 to hand in (8)
8 homework (7)
10 to behave (11)
11 success (5)
12 break, recess, playtime, recreation (6)
13 changing rooms (10)

DOWN

2 pupil, student (6)
3 to answer (9)
4 coloured pencils (7,2,7)
7 to be afraid (5,5)
9 punishment (7)

Education post-16

ACROSS

1 apprenticeship, training, learning (11)
5 career, profession (7)
7 law (at university) (7)
10 full time (1,6,8)

DOWN

1 part time (1,6,7)
2 to leave (5)
3 perspective, prospect, outlook (11)
4 knowledge (13)
6 beginning, start (8)
8 apprentice (8)
9 academy (8)
11 to achieve (6)

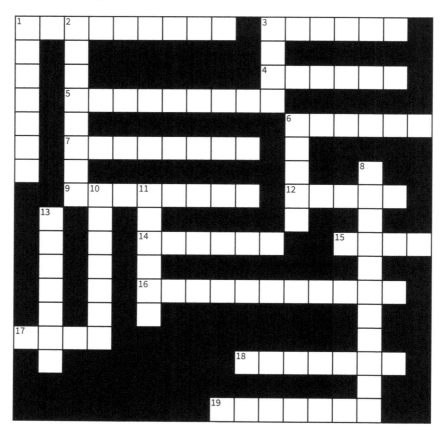

ACROSS

1 to find (9)
3 post (6)
4 university degree (6)
5 housewife (3,2,4)
6 wages, salary (6)
7 army (8)
9 aim, objective (8)
12 line (5)
14 unemployed (6)
15 boss (4)
16 to be unemployed (5,2,4)
17 unemployment (4)
18 working (7)
19 soldier (7)

DOWN

1 company (7)
2 waiter (8)
3 appointment (4)
6 stamp (5)
8 work from home (11)
10 firefighter (7)
11 job, employment (6)
13 serviceman, soldier (7)

ACROSS

1 commerce, trade (8)

5 workman (6)

7 to be in charge of (10,2)

9 to triumph, to succeed (8)

11 engineer (civil/mechanical) (9)

12 bank-teller, cashier (6)

14 writer (8)

15 application (job) (9)

DOWN

1 butcher (9)

2 hope, prospect (11)

3 to get, to obtain (7)

4 cook (8)

6 to earn (5)

8 person in charge (9)

10 translator (9)

12 postman (7)

13 envelope (5)

Jobs, career choices and ambitions (3)

ACROSS

1 to have a go, to try (6)
3 call (7)
4 letter (5)
5 nurse (9)
10 ready (6)
11 veterinary surgeon (11)
12 executive, officer (9)

DOWN

2 to fill in (8)
4 contract (8)
6 employee, worker (8)
7 journalism (10)
8 accountant (8)
9 merchant, retailer, shop owner (11)
10 painter, artist (6)

1

```
COMO          PORESO
O I           A      I
M S    P      R      N      M
O  MENOSQUE   E      E      I
   O   O      C      M      E
   A   R   S  I      B      N
       Q   I  D      A      T
MÁSQUE Q   COMPARARAS   R   A
A    í U      A  O   G      A
Y AQUE E      T  C   O      S
O    U     TANTO
R    E     TAMBIÉN
           É
     DEMASIADO
     BASTANTE
```

2

```
NINGUNO
A   I    A      P      SINO
D   E    DADOQUE      E
I   PARA R      GÚN         T
E   N    U      A           A
N   U    N      L      A    M
C   N    Y  A   D      P    P
HASTA    Y  N   D      A    O
HACIA    POROTROLADO   R    C
I   N    O      T      T
C   D    R      E      E
I   U           D      A
A   D           É      R
    ADEMÁS             Q
         SIN   ESDECIR U
```

3

```
QUISIERA      H
    A      HAYQUE
 V  B      C       D
PODER   Q  E    P  A
 L  R  SEGUIR   O  R
 V     E        N  S
NECESITAR       E  E
 R     R  ECHAR    C
 S  D  D  R        U
EMPEZAR HACERSE    E
    B  R        N  N
 S  E       I   T  T
OCURRIR P  IR      A
    R   ACABARDE   E
SER H   S
  R HACERFALTA
    Y
```

4

```
CIENTOUNO         DO
I     R           OS     P
E  SETECIENTOS     CH    R
N  C  I           HO     I
   QUINTO  ON  VE CO     M
   A  TA    N  EI  O     E
   T        C  IN   VEINTIOCHO
DOCE        E  T    H
O     TRESCIENTOS
DIEZ        N  T
I     UNO      DO   C
E  CATORCE   S OCE  U
N  I  R      V      A
T  N  E   VEINTE N  T
O  C  C            R
S NOVENTA OCTAVO
```

SOLUTIONS

5

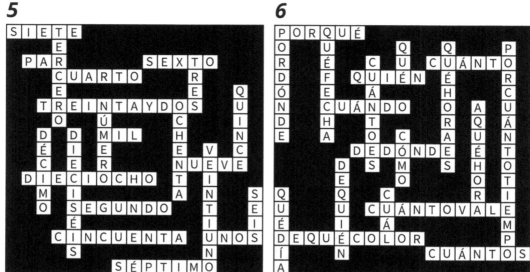

6

7

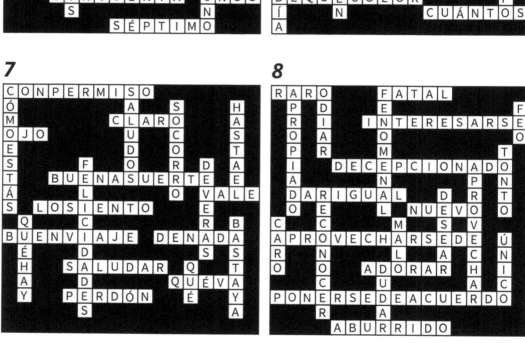

8

SOLUTIONS

9

```
D I S T I N T O             V
E           A G R A D A B L E   N
C A L I D A D             T
E         I   P         A
P R E C I O S O   M   A       J
C         P   S       A
I     D   V A L E R L A P E N A
O     E   F   E   R   S
N     C D O   S   I   P   P
A P R E C I A R   S   O   P   R
N     P S   T   I   M   E   O
T     C F   U   O   A   R   F
E     I R   N   N   L   A   U
      O U   A   N       R   N
      N T   D   T           D
      B A R A T O   S E N C I L L O
      R R
```

10

```
F A S T I D I A R         R
Á   E   N             R
N   T E N E R R A Z Ó N
I   I   E       Z
L   R E M O C I O N A N T E   S
    R   S       C       P
    P A R E C E R   R   L
    U           E   Í   É
I   N           I   B   N
N S E G U R O   A       D
E   R       I N Ú T I L   I
G U A Y     A   T   E   D
U R     D E C I R       D
R   U       G   V I E J O
O P I N A R O   U
        O   H O R R O R O S O
```

11

```
A L E G R A R S E D E
B   S       I
U   T   E   C   V
R   A   S O R P R E N D I D O
R   R   T   E   R
I   A   E   E   Ú T I L
R   F   R   R   I
S   A   E   R   D   E
E   V   N   B   O   S
    O   C   U       T
    R   O   E       U
    E N C A N T A R   P
        T   O       E
        R           N
E S T A R D E A C U E R D O   D
                    O
```

12

```
S I G U I E N T E
I           O     D   S O L O
E           D E N U E V O
M E S       A     N   B
P       B R E V E   T A R D E
R A T O     Í     R   E
E   E   P O R A Ñ O   O
    M   R       D       D
    P   I     A N T E S   H O Y
    O   N     A   A       S
    R   C A D A   R       V
    A   I       D   V E Z
    D   P O C A S V E C E S   C
    A   I               E
    T O D O S L O S M E S E S
        Í
        A
```

SOLUTIONS

13

OTOÑO
TARDAR
MAÑANA
DURANTE
PRIMAVERA
SIGLO
PASADO
LENTO
AESODE
DURAR
PORVENIR
MIENTRASTANTO

14

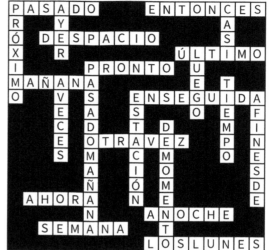

15

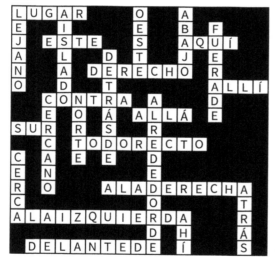

16

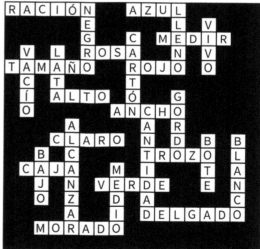

17

18

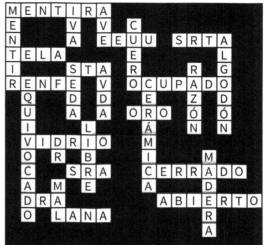

19

20

SOLUTIONS

21

22

23

24

25

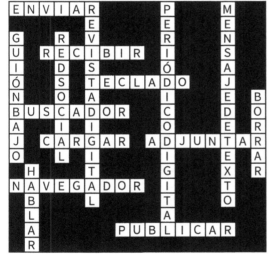

26

27

28

SOLUTIONS

29

30

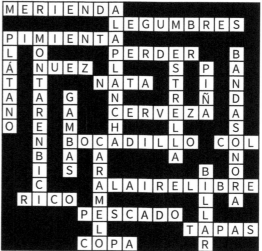

31

32

33

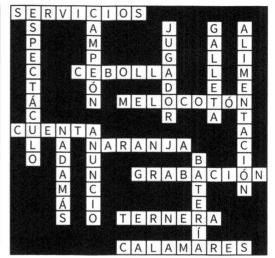

34

35

36

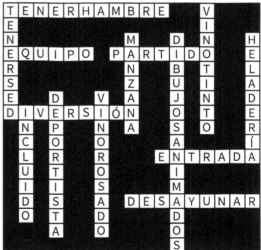

SOLUTIONS

37

Crossword solution grid containing:
JUGUETE · T · CORRIDA · GAUCHO · TOMATE · PAPÁNOEL · FIESTA · DISFRAZ · VILLANCICO · REYES · SANTA · SUERTE · BANDERA · FERIA · PASO · TORERO · MARIACHI

38

Crossword solution grid containing:
PROBARSE · PONERSE · BOLSO · SUBIR · LIMPIO · CORBATA · MICROONDAS · FREGADERO · ESTANCO · SUELO · ESTANTERÍA · ENTARSE · ASEO · PLANTA · LUEGO · REBAJAR · ÁRBOL · DEBER · LADO · HABITANTE · LUZ

39

Crossword solution grid containing:
SALÓN · PRECIO · BLUSA · ESPEJO · CAMA · CÓMODO · PLAZA · HORNO · PAGA · MESA · CINE · PELUQUERÍA · JOYERÍA · VENTA · PLANTABAJA · PLATOS

40

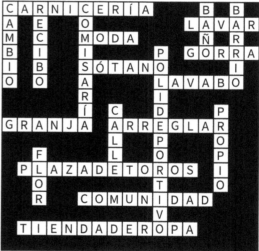

Crossword solution grid containing:
CARNICERÍA · B · B · CAMBIO · LAVAR · MODA · GORRA · SÓTANO · LAVABO · GRANJA · ARREGLAR · PROPIO · FLOR · PLAZADETOROS · COMUNIDAD · TIENDADEROPA

84

41

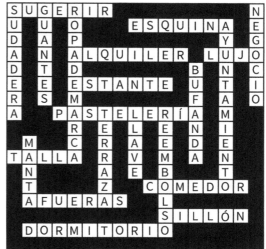

42

43

44

SOLUTIONS

45

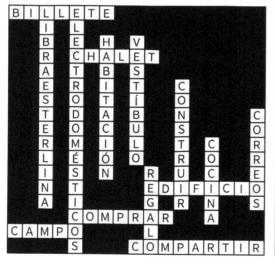

46

47

48

49

50

51

52

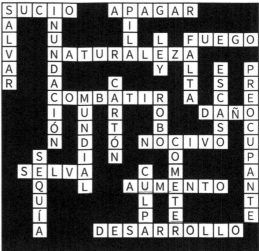

SOLUTIONS

53

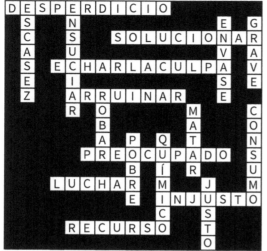

54

55

56

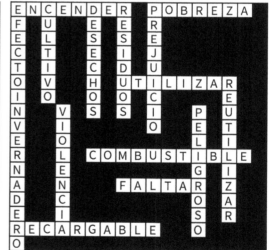

57

ALEMANIA ... VUELO
GUÍA ... BRITÁNICO
VÍA ... RECUERDO
INSOLACIÓN
MOTOR ... PARAR

58

NORTEAMERICANO ... ESTACIÓN
PARADA ... GRECIA ... INDIVIDUAL ... ADUANA
DOBLAR
BAÑARSE ... COGER ... VIAJE
BUSCAR ... GUÍA ... RETIRARSE
GALES ... SACODEDORMIR
QUEJARSE

59

PLAYA
FERROCARRIL
CARNETDECONDUCIR
CAMIÓN
ALEMÁN ... SEÑAL
GALÉS
SITIO
COCHE
VIAJERO
ABANICO

60

RESERVAR ... FICHA
TORCER ... SACAR
PASOSUBTERRÁNEO
ESQUÍ
NOFUMADOR
LIBRE
EUROPA
AMBIENTE
EXCURSIÓN ... AUTOCAR

SOLUTIONS

61

S I T I O   L
R   P O S T A L
L   P   N   R
A G E N C I A D E V I A J E S
N   S   R   G
D   I   P   R E G R E S A R   E
A   Ó   E   S   E   S
    N   N   F O L L E T O   E
    C   S   A   Q   S
    O   I   M O N T A Ñ A   R U E D A
    M   Ó   I   Ñ
    P   L L E G A D A   A
    L   I N G L É S
    E   A
    T A R J E T A
    A

62

B R O N C E A R S E
  E L   S
  L   D   C Á M A R A
C A M I N O   L
  J   R   C   B O N O B Ú S
  A   R   C   E
  R   E   I   I R L A N D É S
  S   C   A   U   V
  E   C   G   A
        I   R E S E R V A   C
C A R N E T   J   A
        Ó   Q U E J A   C
                V   I
                V   O
I S L A S C A N A R I A S   N
                I   E
        I N S T A L A C I O N E S

63

A M A N O D E R E C H A
    E   R   P E R D E R
    P   U   A
    O   C   R
L L E V A R   E S C O C É S
    T   P   R   A   H
C R U C E S A R O   R   A B I T A C I Ó N
A   S   A   O   C   O N S
M   P A S A J E R O   N   S   I
B   C   D   S A L I D A
I   U   O   G   T
A   Á   R   N   A
R   T   Ó   C
        I N G L A T E R R A   Ó N
        C
    V O L V E R
        S

64

F R A N C É S
        A   G
    C R E M A S O L A R   R
        R   P   A
        E   E   N
        T A R D A R   R   B
        E   I   D   R
A   R   S   E   E
V I S T A   P   C O N D U C I R   T
E   O   O   S   A
R   M   N   I D A Y V U E L T A   Ñ
I   B   I   A
A   R   B
D   I   A L O J A M I E N T O
O   L
    L P A P E L H I G I É N I C O

65

```
COMERCIO
 P
 T R A B A J A D O R
 A
A R T E D R A M Á T I C O
L A L L E R . . . . O . . . . . . T
E . . I . . . . . C . . . . . . A
M . . R . . . C . I . . . . . R
Á . . E . G I M N A S I A . E
N . . C . E . . A . . . . . A
 . . T . N . . . D
 . N O T A . . . . . .
 . . R . C . . D
 . . . . I D I O M A
 . . . . A . B
 F R A N C É S . U
 . . . . . . . J
 . A T E N T O
```

66

```
D E S O B E D I E N T E . . . . O
E . A . . D . N . R . . . . . Í
S . L . . U . T . C A S T I G A R
P . Ó . . C . I . D
A . N . . A . M . U
C . D . . T . I . C H I C L E
H . E . . I . D . I
O . A . . V . A . P R U E B A . L
 A C O S O . . . . . . . . E
 . T . U . B I O L O G Í A . C
 . O . S . . Ó . E . I . Y . T
 . S . P . . N . E . M . U . U
 . . . E . . . . R . N . D . R
 . . . D . . . . . . A . . . A
 A P U N T E S . . . . S . A U L A
 . . . . D . . . . . . I . R
 M O L E S T A R . . . . I
 . . . . R . . C O L E G I O
```

67

```
C A R P E T A
A . E . N . G . . . T . . . . . I
L . S . T E X P L I C A C I Ó N
L . P . N . N . Á . J . . H . S
A . U . D A . . G . E . . A . T
R . E . E . . . I . R . . R . I
S . S . R E G L A . S . . L . T
E . T A . . . . . . . . A R . U
 . A . . . I . . . . . . . . T
 . . . . . B . . . . . . . . O
 A P O Y A R . . N . F
 . E . . O L V I D A R
L E T R A . . . V . L
 . M . T . . . E . T
 D I S E Ñ A R . L . A P O Y O
 S . M . . . . . . R
A P R O B A R
```

68

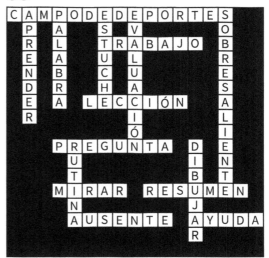

```
C A M P O D E D E P O R T E S . O
P . A . . S . V . . . . . . . . B
R . L . T R A B A J O . . . . R
E . A . U . L . . . . . . . . E
N . B . C . U . . . . . . . . S
D . R . H . A . . . . . . . . A
E . A L E C C I Ó N . . . . L
R . . . . . . I . . . . . . I
 . . . . . . . Ó . . . . . . E
 . P R E G U N T A . . D . N
 . R . . . . . . . . I . T
 . U . . . . . . . . B
 M I R A R . R E S U M E N
 . N . . . . . . . J
 . A U S E N T E . A Y U D A
 . . . . . . . . . R
```

SOLUTIONS

69

```
BOLÍGRAFO
      R
 MOCHILA
        C CONDUCTA
    P   A
    E   ESFORZARSE
    D   A        E
TERMINAR R       P   F
 X  R            A   A
 A  PASARLALISTA T   L
 M  R            A   T
 E  EXPLICAR     R   A
 N  S
    T
 SALADEPROFESORES
    D
    GOLPEAR
```

70

```
MASCULINO
L   O   Á
U   N   PREGUNTAR
M   T   I
N   E   C
O   S   E ENTREGAR          T
    T   S                   E
    A   DEBERES             N
    R   E          C        E
        COMPORTARSE         R
 ÉXITO  O          S        M
        L          T        I
 RECREO R          I        E
        R          G        D
        VESTUARIOS          O
        S
```

71

```
APRENDIZAJE
      E        P
      J        E
   C  CARRERA  R
   O  R        S
   N  A   A    P         C
   O      DERECHO        O
   C  A   A    C         M
ATIEMPOCOMPLETO          I
   M  R   A   O  I        E
   I  E   A   G  V        N
   E  N   D   R  A        Z
   N  D   E   A           O
   T  I   M   R
   O  Z   I
   S      A
```

72

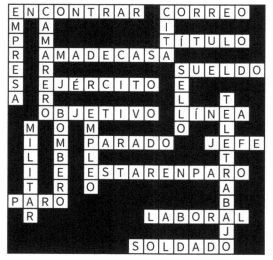

```
ENCONTRAR   CORREO
M   A             I
P   A             TÍTULO
R   AMADECASA
E   R             SUELDO
S   EJÉRCITO      E
A   R             L        T
    OBJETIVO      LÍNEA
M   O   M         O        L
I   M   PARADO             JEFE
L   B   L                  T
I   E   ESTARENPARO
T   R   O                  A
PARO                       B
R           LABORAL        J
            SOLDADO
```

92

73

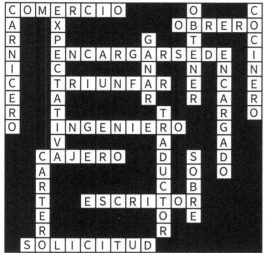

74

Lightning Source UK Ltd.
Milton Keynes UK
UKHW031822140222
398681UK00008B/1546

9 781838 272111